I'm Not a Homewrecker, Opportunist Maybe!

Sometimes people are placed in our lives to make up for others.
"Who's really at fault, me, him, us or them?"

Karla Davis-Luster

ISBN: 9798376920855

Dedication

In loving memory of Mae Helen Thomas
March 21, 1937-August 25, 2022

Thank you mom for inseminating in me that I could
be anything. Thanks to you, I became me!

RIP

TABLE OF CONTENTS

CHAPTER 1

We Twee, We Chuck Em'

YES, THIS IS me. The so-called MISTRESS telling my side of the story about my life and giving my opinion about the shit that was written about me in "The Woman Tells." I'm a realist that speaks my truth. So, let's get to it. I'm not that bitch in a bubble that's unable to think or do anything without a laid-out script. Unlike her, the wife that narrated bullshit in "The Woman Tells," I was not blessed with a life modeled after the stories you watch on tv, social media and the news. I sound angry because my life is quite the contrary. Keep in mind, not everyone is fortunate enough to be born or fall into wealth. Most people and families struggle somewhere along the way. I am a firm believer that you are responsible for making your own luck. The perfect life, as society would have you think goes something like this. The norm is that you are a product of a two-parent household with one or both parents having college degrees, both have great jobs, a savings account and goals laid out. Particularly, for the children. They are surrounded with a support base of fake friends and grandparents that you visit for the summer when not attending an expensive ass camp. Part of those goals would consist of a 529 plan that was started at birth. Your school selections would be like selecting a house or a car. Only the best. The top of the line of course with only one question after choosing, "Who has the best one?" God forbid If you were not already on a list to be accepted into the who's who school of who's who. These would be the schools that the average kid would not be a candidate for or would even be a consideration due to their parent's lack of social and economic stability. Meaning that your parents tax bracket would be looked at as below poverty. Competency, skills, ability, and experience would have no bearing on the outcome of acceptance. Final seats at the table usually would be decided by which parent could exude the most power, donate the largest gift to the school or has the largest political influence. Meals and bills would never be a concern. Only what's the latest and greatest, how much faster can I obtain the best before the Brown's, and should I get this colour or that colour? Here's another analogy. The question would also be," Is my sitter an au pair, childcare worker, older brother or sister, cousin or drunk out of work uncle? If your answer is out of work uncle, society say's "you aren't shit." Let me be clear and upfront before I share my life's background. Her husband came at me and accepted my number. At what point is his bum ass held accountable. Women always want to bash the other woman. Well, if your whacked ass was more interesting and fly, maybe he wouldn't need to look my way. So, if I were one to give a fuck about any of the shit society say's or think, then I guess I would have problems. Well, guess what? I don't. My story started something like this.........

I was born in the decade where women were still domestic home-makers. Everyone pitched in to help maintain the house. Mom made home cooked meals and baking was still part of the family tradition. Laundry, dishes, and basic household chores were divided amongst the family unit. As a kid you had certain things you needed to get done before allowed playtime. Teachers were still in charge. A ruler or paddle to the knuckles or butt was the norm. God help you if your teacher called your house. You got your ass beat twice.

As an aggressive female, it started young. I got quite a few calls to the house. My disruptive attitude stemmed from my home life. It was not a good one. I was the middle child of four siblings. I had an older sister and two baby brothers that were twins. To my surprise, I learned in later years that there were more children. Dad was extremely popular. My mother was a plain matronly lady. She was his hidden treasure. I guess his main woman. However, he talked to her in a manner of disparage. I vowed that this would never be me. I hated how submissive she was to a man that treated her like shit, but once again that was her life. Getting back to my younger years, I met my best friend right around entering sixth grade. I can remember my family had just moved to what was supposed to be a better neighborhood. As a young child, I spent my years being raised in the projects with my mom and siblings. Dad was out galivanting around with his bitches. As I mentioned, we learned he had them later. Mom of course knew in her heart all the time, but once again, turned her head. His life extended everywhere beyond us with additional families he had been keeping around.

Well, how I met my best friend was very weird. I was sitting on my porch, and she walked pass and said hi. I was not use to people being friendly. Even at an early age growing up in the projects you learned how to always be on the defense. I spoke back. That day, I sat on the porch until dark. Then I went into the house. My mom was still trying to get us settled in, still putting away boxes. We had pizza for dinner. My mom always worked extremely hard to manage everything. Along with getting things together, tending to the twins and trying to figure out what my dad was up to kept her busy and tired. This left me open to do whatever I wanted. My older sister was several years ahead of me, doing her own thing with no time for a tag alone. As time passed me and my newly found friend began to hang out and became close, sister friends. I can remember starting my new school. I became extremely popular quick with the great genes, bodied up and long hair. Every little pervert wanted to know who I was. It also helped that my friend was also a cutie pie, she was very fair skinned to the point she could be a passer, a cheer star and mischievous as hell. Her parents were these contemporary unfit goof balls that tend to be incredibly open minded, carefree, and inattentive to their child's wild behavior. Hanging with her was so much fun. We got into so much stuff. We would occasionally hang at her house, because her parents were barely ever there, and it was a lot nicer than mine. They were living well. My friend had an older brother. He and his friends would always be there getting high, drinking, and partying with girls over. You name it, it was happening in that house. Her brother had to be about 16 or 17 years old. He and his friends would allow us to drink and smoke with them as well. Her brother would say that it helped to shape us into real woman. I noticed that he was always friendly with me. To the point it made me uncomfortable. Stay tuned because yes there was an episode related to hanging at that house that happened to change my life forever.

I can remember back in 8th grade when we would attend the Junior High School "Sock Hop's". My friend and I would dress alike. We had a group of friends that we called the "Pretty Girls Inc." It was about six of us. We would walk into the school dances, dressed alike, looking fly, and shut it down. We had lots of other girls that despised us and wanted to fight us. Luckily for us, one of the six girls in our little club was this hugh he-man girl that didn't take any shit. She just wanted to be part of our clique. She was not a pretty girl; however, she was overly sweet, strong, and aggressive. She was on the cheer squad, very athletic, usually the base with stunts and she was our protection when we needed it. Most people did not fuck with her. That was all the reason to keep her around. I can remember when some bullshit broke out at a "Sock Hop" we were attending. It went something like this. My girl went to the bathroom to use it, obviously comb her hair and to make sure that she was still the queen she thought she was. In the interim, the rest of us was on the floor dancing with either someone we called ourselves kicking it with or pushing up on somebody else's man. Prior to going to the bathroom, my friend had just left the corner making out with a rival's man. Where in the shig-diggaty were the chaperones. Somewhere high or making out with another teacher themselves. Pissed because they were on duty. This was definitely "Cooley High" all over again. Shitty school, shitty staff. It's called going to school in the hood. Back to my point, my girl went to the bathroom and there is where it started. Three girls entered the bathroom to confront her. Immediately they began arguing with my friend calling her names selling woof tickets on what they were going to do. My friend recalled, in the midst of what was about to break bad remembered one conversation that my mom had with us one afternoon while discussing how much the girls at our school disliked us. My mom's words were, if you are ever in trouble and outnumbered, make sure you at least make one of them pay should a fight break out. The more they hit you, the more you wham on the one that's paying ass and don't let her go until they let you go. Believe it or not, this came from the woman that was submissive and easy going. My friend listened and took it to heart because she knew that they were going to fight. She threw the first punch and grabbed the one girl that was in her face and started beating her ass. Just a reminder, my friend was athletic and in great shape. Although that did not save her, she beat the living shit out of one of the girls. Once my friend grabbed one of them, her friends began to annihilate my girl. But she held on to the one. They were kicking her, hitting her and the last blow was a toilet lid to my friend's head which knocked her out as they continued to stump her. By this time, the commotion was heard, and everyone began to rush to the bathrooms. Teachers were trying to push us back. It was a mess. Security was everywhere. My posse was crying and kicking trying to get to her. They handcuffed the girls fighting my friend and was taking them out to go to the station. The one girl was fucked up, but walking. Still, they had not brought my friend out yet. The ambulance arrived. They began to attend to the one girl and the others rush inside the restroom. The principal was over the speaker dismissing the party telling everyone to go home. I finally calmed down enough to call her brother, which got a hold of her parents. While talking to them, they brought my friend out on a stretcher, bloody as hell, unconscious and fighting for her life. I also called my mom to let her know what had happened. I told her we were going to go to the hospital. My mom said that she was on her way. My oldest sister stayed with the twins. By the time we arrived at the hospital, the lobby, outside, everywhere was full. People crying. Her parents and brother had made it there. We took longer getting there by bus. This was the longest night of my life. It turns out that they immediately took my friend to surgery. She was bleeding on the brain and was in critical condition. Fate has it that she made it through surgery. She spent several months in the hospital, therapy, and a rehabilitation facility before coming home to be homed schooled the remainder of her 8th grade year. She was able to physically attend the graduation. I was so happy that we had already been accepted into the same high school and was looking forward to getting back to hanging out. The girls that jumped her had a rough ending as well. The bitch that hit my friend in the head got sent to a juvenile home until she was 18. The other two girls got off with two years of community service due to a technicality that my friend threw the first blow. They claimed they were not going to fight her, just argue, and had she not hit first, they were just going to argue. Everyone knew that it was bullshit, but due to no witnesses for my friend, they got off easy. My thoughts were, "Every dog has its day." I'm just glad my friend was able to come home. This was a great summer despite the fact that my friend had restrictions until she could be released with a clean bill of health. I attended some of her doctor's appointments with her. I at least went and sat in the lobby while she was being seen. Her brother continued to be overly friendly. Her parents slowed down a minute to take care of her more closely. My household continued to be as normal as could be expected. It was an exciting time because my sister had finished her senior year and was graduating as well. She attended prom. Boy was she gorgeous. My sister was part of the young LGBTQ community. Of course, during this time, there was no sophisticated name for this alternative lifestyle. It was a time still life was challenging and not as excepting. Her prom date was equally beautifully styled. She had been accepted to a great college and was preparing to leave. We did all the expected things we could for a graduate. It was a double whammy due to my graduation was happening as well. Keep reading. This is one of many stories I will tell.

"YOUR VIBE ATTRACTS YOUR TRIBE"

CHAPTER 2

Fam!

I WOKE UP early to banging pots and lots of noise. Today was the day my sister was making her way to a semi new lifestyle. She had been packing and getting ready for the last year. Talking about ready to move on. If that wasn't a sign, then the sky isn't blue. I for one could not blame her for wanting more. We lived check to check with what my mom made. My dad contributed when he felt like it. Depending on when we saw him. My sister was super smart and had been awarded a full academic scholarship. I was incredibly happy for her, but sad to see her go. I knew moving forward my mom would be expecting me to help with the twins. Not that I mined, but I still enjoyed hanging with my friends. We slowed down a bit after my friend's ordeal with those girls. We too were starting a new endeavor into high school. I was nervous. New place, new people. Starting over trying to be accepted. I did not know what to expect. Would I be as popular in High school as in Junior High? Or would I be the low girl on the totem pole in the looks category? This was one of the most popular schools in our city, known for pretty girls, athletic programs, and academics. Exceedingly rare for a school to be known for three out of three in the most important categories across the board. At least in our minds. My girl had been working hard to get back to her total self. She was guaranteed a spot on the State Champs cheerleading team. So, in retrospect, she already had her place in being the new hot girl solidified. The jury was still out as to where I would land in the popularity contest. I guess I needed to start thinking about if I had any talents. I was a great dancer so trying out for the dance squad was not a bad idea. My friend and I were both lucky to attend this school. It was a private school with donors that insisted that a percentage of underprivileged kids have an opportunity to attend. To be accepted you had to be qualified and exceed in one or more areas of the criteria. Of course, there were only so many spots offered to our graduating class. As fate would have it, not many of our classmates were interested and applied. Everyone got in except three people. My principal had a lottery among our students that were interested and that met the standards. There were four slots and seven applied. My girl and I both got pulled. We found out that we were accepted prior to her mishap.

Back to my sister, she was so excited this day. I was walking behind her like a puppy. I was bummed about her leaving. My mom had rented a van so that she could take my sister to school with all her things. My two brothers and my mom's friend tagged along to help put things together. My sister had a trunk party. She received most of the things she needed. She also was already set up with a work study job to help her with extra finances. She was set. My mom's friend was some guy that had grown up with her like a brother. He was a handy man, married with children and awfully close to us like a real uncle. Sometimes I felt like he felt sorry for my mom and her situation. His wife was genuinely nice as well. Occasionally she would babysit us when we were young. Mostly my sister and I. By the time the twins came along we were old enough to help. More so my sister. My mom's friend and family lived about two blocks away. That made life easier and more convenient for my mom having them live so close. I stayed behind with the wife and kids for a couple of days until my mom and brothers were to returned. I unfortunately could not go because of an orientation happening for first-year students at my school during my sisters move to college. It was simple for me to go with my best friend and family to the orientation while mom was away. My play uncle was flying back late tomorrow because he had work the following day. My mom and the twins were staying an additional day to make sure my sister was set; they were driving back in the rented van by themselves. My sister's school was 11 hours away. We saw them off.

I woke up the next day excited with butterflies in my stomach. It was orientation day. My best friend and her mom were going to pick me up at 11:30 to head to our new school for the festivities. My play aunt was up already making a little something for breakfast. I was so nervous I was afraid to eat. We had eggs, bacon, a biscuit and orange juice. My mom had purchased me some new jeans and top for the orientation. She really could not afford to do it, but I guess it was a means to cheer me up with my sister leaving. After breakfast I got dressed making sure that I looked my best. I had no idea what to expect. School activities were planned for the first-year students from noon until three in the afternoon. This school really knew how to welcome you. I was happy that I at least knew three other people. My best friend and the two other students admitted from my grammar school. Well, it was time. My best friend and mom were outside blowing. Off I went. My girl and I was so excited. When we arrived, the parking lot was already packed. We had to walk quite a way to get there. This school was hugh. They really put on a production. The first activity started out in the gymnasium where every school team, club and organization were there pitching their squad. The school band was there loud and quite annoying trying to play the latest hits, sounding off. The program allowed us to break into groups for about an hour to sample their curriculum.

The school offered such studies as Foreign Languages, Auto Shop, Home Economics, Barbering and Beauty Esthetics. I was so pumped. Life could not be better right now. After leaving the orientation, my friends mom took us out to eat at this burger place not too far from the school. As we walked in, I noticed that a lot of upper classmates were there hanging out. You could tell by the school jackets. Of course, I locked eyes with one. He was popular with his posse. My girl noticed that he kept staring at me. I think he was on the basketball team. I remembered seeing him in the gym during the rally. He would not dare come over with my friend's mom sitting with us. I'm sure I will see him soon at school. That made me even more excited to start this new venture. My friend was getting a lot of stares as well. I thought to myself. We might still be the shit. We headed home. I went back to their house for a while. We spent time together in her room talking about what we were going to do, wear and what squads we were going to try out for. Usually, tryouts happened the second week of school. Later, my friend and her brother walked me back to my play uncle's house where I was staying. I got back just in time to ride with his wife to pick him up from the airport. I slept there and back in the car. They had two younger kids. 5th and 7th grade. When we made it back to the house, my uncle and wife asked if I was ok and how did the orientation go. We chatted. My uncle gave me the 411 about the car ride down. Apparently my sister's college was beautiful. He also told me that my sister and mom had words about her coming home for the holidays. My sister really was not interested in coming back. She said she would rather stay and work and make money. In his opinion, my mom was terribly angry and started in on her. Other than that, he said that it went well. My sister's roommate was this Chinese girl. A little weird for my sister, but my uncle was sure she was nice and afraid to be in the room with my sister. My mom and brothers were able to stay on campus in the guest housing until they were leaving. The school rented them extremely cheap per night. My mom called while we were talking. I got to speak with my sister and brother's. My sister had decided to spend the nights at the guest housing with mom and my brothers until they left. They had one more day and night to be there before driving back. My mom was going to spend the next day with my sister making sure everything was in place as stated. I loved my mom. I got to say good night to my family. Mom said that they would call back tomorrow. I went to bed.

The next morning, I slept in with nothing really planned to do. My play uncle had left for work and his wife had several extra kids over. She babysat for a living. She had great patience. My aunts' kids were outside playing. I was the last one to get up. I was so ready to go home to get ready for this great school I was going to attend. School started next week for me. Mom had promised when she got back, we would shop for school supplies and a couple of outfits. The twins wore uniforms. This was going to be a long rest of the week. I knew mom and those guys were going to call, but usually it was in the late evening before they turned into bed. She and my brothers had only one more night before heading back. She was going to head out early to alleviate night driving. Or as less of it as possible. I called my girl. We decided to hang out. Mom had left me with a little money. My friend always had a little money. I think her brother would give her extra money. He was doing something shady. He had graduated this year like my sister but choose not to go away to school. He was attending a Junior College. I met my friend halfway. We headed to the theatre to see a movie. Afterwards we walked the mall. We spent time together all day until early evening. My uncle's wife had given me a curfew to be back by seven. I followed instructions. I was not trying to get put on punishment. My mom gave long sentences. I did not want my first week of school to be behind bars. I made it back in time for some fried chicken and mash potatoes auntie prepared. My play aunt, I may add. We had fun around the table. My uncle had made it home from work. We all watched a Freddie Kruger movie. My mom and those guys called while we were watching it. My uncle talked to her for a while. I got to speak with my sister again. Later, she told me that she was going to some Frat party. I was shocked because of her recent lifestyle. Of course, I had to hint about that. She said that she thinks that it was just a phase. She had broken it off with her girl and was interested in trying to date guys. I was shocked and confused. However, if it made her happy, who cares. Mom told me that they would be back later than she anticipated because she needed to go with my sister to the Accounting Department before she could pull out. She anticipated that they would get on the road around noon, putting them home at around 12 midnight. She suggested that I spent one more night due to how late they would get in. Man was I mad. My aunt asked to speak with my mom before hanging up. She was telling my mom that she and the boys should spend another night as well because weather was looking bad for her night drive and that she needed to drive during the day. My mom said that it would be fine. She insisted that she would take her time and would pull off if necessary. Well like my aunt said, weather was bad throughout the east coast all day. Uncle left for work, my aunt took in her baby-sitting children, and we, my uncles two kids and I just hung in the house all day. Something about today was very unusual and dark. It was raining like nobody's business. I did not talk to my girl that day. Eventually my mom called to let us know that they were leaving to head home. Weather was ok from where they were currently. She assured my aunt that, the weather looked good and if at all, they stood a chance of missing driving into the rain. Nevertheless, one more un-usual thing happened during the day. My dad stopped by to pick me up. He was back from God knows where. He had come to take me home and said we would grab something to eat for us and enough for mom and the boys. Mom had reached out to him and told him I was ready to go home. I was glad to see him and to go home. Regardless of his absenteeism as a father, I was always a daddy's girl and when I saw him, I was always happy. We went home and ate. We talked and watched a couple of movies. It was about eight. I went to my room and fell asleep. My dad was still watching tv. It had to be around

9:30 at night when the phone rang. The call that would change my life forever. My mom and brothers had been in an accident and killed on impact from a drunk truck driver. It was a head on collision at 75 miles per hour. I remember my dad just falling to his knees. My world was shattered. I do not think I could speak for a week. Our family, what was left of it was crushed. My sister was informed and was flown home by the school. She did not return to school for a minute. Stay tuned as I continue to tell.

CHAPTER 3

After the Rain, came rain

AFTER THE TRAGEDY, life was worthless, unfair, and dark. My sister left this morning heading back to school after a year or so off. After the funeral, her school had approved her to be online for a while to help with her breakdown and our family restructure. Rightfully so, my dad became my guardian. My sister was considered grown. Nonetheless nineteen, motherless and on her own. We were all trying to get some normal in our lives. Whatever that looked like. My first day back to school was going to be next week. I too spent time out of the classroom being homeschooled, counseled, and rehabilitated. My dad had to be strong for us. However, I knew he was hurting. Although he was not always the best father, present, and a sympathetic husband, he did love her. All his street activity did not add up to what he and my mom shared. It was hard on him because he lost his only boys. Out of all the kids he had in the streets, they were all girls. My dad had five girls. Two with my mom. It turns out one by his so-called business partner and two by this chic my mom often suspected he was fooling with in the past. The chic had the audacity to show up to the funeral. My sister got into an argument with her. They almost went to blows. It was a mess. My family on my mom's side got involved. What a circus. No matter the situation, my dad stepped up when it counted. Their relationship was their own. We were trying to mend the pieces and push forward. That's something I know my mom would have wanted. The house was quiet after my sister left.

Speaking of my sister, she went through a lot. She started having dizzy spells after the funeral to the point she would black out. The doctor called it "stress." He thought it was a coping mechanism for her to deal with the tragedy. She was close to my mom. They argued but they were close. I prayed that when she returned to school that she would find some form of happiness. Throughout her life I felt like she struggled with her identity. Her school had a lot to offer. It was best that now since her health was better that she got back into the groove. She was excited because when she returned to school, she had decided that she was going to try to join a Sorority. Of course, "AKA." My mom before her passing encouraged her to find something that she liked and to go for it. Her words were, "If you never try, that's a 100% guaranteed miss." Once she arrived that night, she called back to say she had made it. The dope thing about my dad was that he had surprised her with a car to take back to school. It's no telling how he paid for it. I know that he was trying to overcompensate for the absence of our mom. He promised to buy me one once I graduated high school. This year went by extremely fast. Man, another school year was upon us. I could not wait. I was excited because my dad had given me money to go school shopping. I had not seen my girl in a minute. She spent a lot of her summer away at an aunt's house with cousins in LA. She called me a couple of times. She told me that she met this older guy out in LA. It sounded like he had her on some other stuff that I was not feeling. I'm sure today she will have a lot to tell. According to her, the biggest thing was that she lost her virginity. I guess I wasn't shocked. We were both a little fast. I went to bed early because I wanted morning to hurry around.

I was dressed and waiting on her to swoop me up by 10am. Her mom was giving us a ride to the mall. Over the last year she had recovered 100% from the injuries she sustained from those girls jumping her back in grammar school. We arrived at the mall and began shopping, talking, and hanging out. It looked like everyone from our hood was there shopping for school. We also spent some time in the gaming facility there. Everyone was glad to see each other. We were catching up on what was going on in our lives. My girl at one point even thought that she was pregnant by the guy in LA. She was bummed because she had not heard from him since she returned home. She told me that he would borrow money from her that her parents would send her, and that she never got it back. She also mentioned that he had roughed her up before. Me being me, I had to tell her what I really thought. Starting with the fact I thought that he was a fucking looser and that he did not know how to treat a woman. She got a little angry and made excuses for him, but in the end after the ghosting happened, she started to agree with me. Well, it happened, as we were getting ready to leave the mall, being there for six hours, we ran into the two of three girls that jumped my girl a while back. I knew they were still on probation, but you would not have known it by their behavior. They immediately started talking shit. This time the scales were tilted in my girl's favor. We were still with a lot of our friends we ran into in the mall. They had some guy with them. Another fight broke out. This time it was just a lot of swinging, swearing, and pushing. Mall security was "Johnny on the Spot" to break it up. No one got arrested. We disbursed home. School was in two days. We didn't have to worry about seeing them at school because my girl and I was attending a prep school we were privileged enough to land a scholarship. That night when we got home or after her mom and her dropped me off, I told her that I would call her once I ate dinner with my dad and got settled. I finally called her. She was really talking crazy. She said that if it was the last thing she did, she was going to make sure that those bitches paid for what they had done. Her crazy whacked out ass brother was in the background instigating. They were planning to set up one of the girls. We all knew where she lived. I was trying to get them to calm down. I told her brother that if he got caught, he would do time because he was now over 18. He got mad and told me to shut up and that I was soft. Me with my smart mouth told him to shut the fuck up talking to me and that he was stupid. He promised to make me remember what I had said. Her brother had gone down the thug path. However, I was not afraid of him, and he was just talking shit with his creepy ass.

Monday rolled around quick. First day back to school, I had to make a statement. We had planned to start off fly out the gate. We had a couple of classes together and most importantly we had lunch together. The year was going well except for me struggling in Geometry. My girl was a brainiac. She could hang out, not study and still pass classes. I was smart, but I had to put in a little time in the books. My dad had lofty expectations for me. I know that my mom looking down did as well. Homecoming was coming up. So, we had to get our dresses together. At this prep school, people went with dates. Both of us had been asked by a couple of guys from the basketball team. They were seniors. We were cutie pies so there you have it. Of course, history repeats itself. Most of the girls there did not like us. We had a posse and was always taking somebody's man. Like my girl, I lost my virginity to a boy who lived around the house. We had gone to grammar school together. We were fast and thought we had it all together. The night of the dance little did I know was going to be another life changing event. I guess throughout this novel I will share various stories that help to affect my decision making.

I was dressed in a short ass red dress, back out, nails done like a grown ass woman and ready to party at the school dance. My girl's dress was red too. It was both of our favorite colours. We looked like two full blown women. If you did not know us. You would think we were between eighteen and twenty-two. Upon leaving the house, my dad said, "I'm not sure I'm comfortable with the way you are dressed." Of course, I told him that he was old fashioned, and that all the girls were dressing this way. Bla, bla bla. My date had come to our house. We were meeting my girl and her date at her house and planning to ride together. Before we were allowed to leave, my dad gave my date the third degree. He insinuated that he had a gun. Funny right, typical. When we arrived at my girl's house, her date was already there waiting. So, we came in and I marched to the back to see my girl's dress. Of course. her parents were out. Her brother was there with some friends drinking, getting high and playing cards. They had a party of their own going on. When I walked past her brother and his friends, they started making noises, whistling, and starring. He himself had a weird ass perverted look on his face. I didn't pay him any attention as usual. My dad had agreed to let me spend the night at my girl's house because he too was going out. He was my parent, but he was not as strict as my mom had been. He was like my girls' parents. Very inattentive. We left for the dance in separate cars because both guys had driven. At the dance, we had fun, laughed, danced, drank, and ate. After the dance there was a after party at one of the kids houses. We all jumped in cars in went. It was getting late, and I was tired. I told my girl let's go. She was not ready, so she gave me her keys to go ahead. My date was nice, fine, but a square. I think he was afraid of me. So, we left, and he dropped me at my girl's house. My life would never be the same.

I went in. Her brother and friends were still there. It looked like more of his friends had come over. It looked like the room stopped when I came through the door. Her brother knew that I was spending the night. I think he was surprised to not see my girl with me. He asked where she was? I replied, she wanted to stay. It felt weird. God also gives you that intuition and sense, even at an early age. I should have waited on her or left and headed home. Both were nudging at me, I thought, which were the lesser of the two evils. Should I stay with a house full of drugged out losers or should I walk home in the dark alone. Wrong choice again. Apprehensive and frightened, I retired in my girl's room. They were so loud that I could not sleep. Here it was the devil at my door. I should have locked it but young unaware and stupid I didn't. One of her brothers' friends wondered into the room. Yes, it happened to me, it was the longest night of my life. The music was loud so no one could hear what was going on. He made me do things I dare not repeat. I think he had evil on his mind the minute I came in. Another one wondered into the room, and they locked the door. They were choking me and slapping me. After they finished with me, they threatened me and told me if I said anything that it would be the last day I had breathe. I never figured out why her brother never checked on me. I wondered if he had them do it because of how I had talked to him. I was scared to leave the room. Hours later, it sounded like everyone had left. I got dressed. After putting on my pants, they got messed up. I was bleeding. My girl's room was on the first floor. It was a weird kind of house. I raised her window and jumped out to avoid walking out just in case they were still there. My friend still had not made it home. I ran until I made it home a couple of blocks away. My dad was still out. I went in the house, locked the doors, took a shower, curled up in my bed with a knife crying, and scared with a secret I would take to my grave. Little did I know that the nightmare would not end there. I asked God why he had forsaken me. It seemed like mishaps and tragedy followed me. The next day and the next several days I stayed in my room. My dad thought that I was not feeling well from my monthly. Thank God for family. During the early passing of my mom. I had become close to my dad's sister. She had committed to me that if I needed her, or if I needed a woman to talk to, she would always be there. So, I reached out to her. I did not tell her the full story. Only that I needed to see a doctor for female reasons. She exchanged no words. She made me an appointment for the very next afternoon. We spoke a little. She could tell that I was troubled. She believed it to be boyfriend related. I did not share that I had been raped. The results came back worse than what I thought. Not only was I pregnant but had contracted a STD from one of my violators. Due to the privacy act, it was up to me to share my results with my aunt. I shared both symptoms, but not the truth about what had happened to me. Over the course of the next month, she helped me take care of everything without sharing with my dad. She was still under the impression it was young love gone wrong. I could not share with my dad because at the end of the day, he was from the streets and him knowing could turn out to be a catastrophe. I could not afford to lose another or my only parent. Sharing the truth with my aunt could be bad because out of anger and wanting revenge would drive her to tell. I dreaded men for a while. I was depressed for some time. My girl and I stopped speaking for the remainder of that year. She thought I was mad about her not leaving the party with me. At school I kept to myself the rest of the year. Classmates thought I had gone weird. Deep down inside I felt like her brother knew what his friends had done to me. My dad and I saw him in the grocery store one day. I acted like I did not see him. He just starred. My dad asked why I didn't speak. I just said, I'd rather not say. Two years went by amazingly fast. Yet I never told.

CHAPTER 4

New Day, Old Folly

MY DAD HAD a lot to be proud of. He had two daughters graduating. One from high school and one from college. The last time graduations happened; tragedy followed. So, you can imagine what we were feeling. It was a mixed bag of bittersweet thoughts going on in all of our minds. My sister had moved to the city where she was attending school. She was interning at a major company with a permanent job promise after graduation. She had planned to work and start grad school so that her company could help foot the bill. She was doing well. She hardly ever got home. I had gone to spend some weekends with her over the last year or so. After the situation with those guys at my girl's house. Although I missed hanging out with my use to be BFF, I was afraid and hurt by what had transpired. Part of me resented her for what happened. I vowed that I would never step foot ever again in her house. She had continued to reach out. We had both chosen to attend Columbia University in NY. As far as I knew she was still going. The small amount that we talked, I never got around to asking had she been accepted. I was accepted and set with scholarships and loans. I had plan to work. Although my dad provided for me financially, far more than my mom could do when she was living, I still needed a base. I was moving to NY a month before starting to school with my mom's cousin to start looking for work and spending a little time hanging out with her two daughters. They were around my age. One older and one coming up to her last year of high school. Her oldest daughter attended Syracuse. It would have been nice to know one person at Columbia. Like I said, I was not sure if my girl was still going to attend. I had planned to study Journalism. New York was expensive, but hustling was in my blood from my dad. I was up for the challenge. I was looking forward to a new city, new place, new friends, and new adventures. I was finally trying to move forward and looking forward to putting the rape behind me. My dad had encouraged me to reach out to my girl and talk to her. He had also convinced me to go to prom. I had been asked by several guys but had turned them down. My dad had a large family. Holidays were spent at family houses. I had a boy cousin that was a year younger than me that I bonded with. Him and his sister. She was a sophomore. He had agreed to go to prom with me. We were preparing and discussing our outfits. I decided on navy blue. Unassuming and classy. My dad was willing to go all out. He wanted to make me feel good about everything. Making up for the absence of a mom. I had been very depressed and not myself. My dad had a friend, his boy that had a Bentley. He was going to chauffeur us. My dress was being donated by a hot designer in our city that was sweet on my dad. He knew or had fucked. Every hair stylist, nail, and lash tech from here to the next state knew my dad. So, in the grooming department, we had that on lock. Excitement was starting to creep back into my life. I was extra pumped because I was taking my cousin, a basketball celebrity ranked in the state with a D1 promise. I would be comfortable and have fun because we were buddies. He was extremely good looking like my dad. They all had that handsome look on my dad's side of the family, height, build, charm, and he was my cousin. I didn't give a shit about what he did. He was just family. "Go fam." Prom was two months away, along with graduation and all the activities that would close this chapter of my life.

As I mentioned, my dad had convinced me to return my girls calls. So, I reached out. She answered and was happy to hear from me. She had so many questions. Primarily concerning the friendship. She could not understand why I was so mad. She went on and on, but I could not tell her the truth. I told her to let's just move on and move forward. It turned out that she too had been accepted into Columbia. She still had planned to go and was excited as hell that I was still going. I'm not sure if I was as glad as she was because I kind of liked the fact of starting fresh and clean. But she was my girl at one point, and I did say it would be good to know one person. She asked if I had a roommate yet. Of course not, they had not started sending that out yet. We agreed to send in each other's name to share a room. I did tell her that I was moving a month early to look for a job and to spend time with family. She was sad. Asking if she could go. That was a hard NO. I didn't say it like that. I made up the excuse that my mom's cousin was weird and funny. I would just see her in month. We had planned to shop in New York to decorate our room. I got my mom's cousin to agree to let her come up a couple of days before moving in so that she could take us shopping. The remainder of the year in high school was all about passing classes to start my new life. I felt that a change would help to right all the wrongs that had happened to me. Trying not to remember the bad decision I made not to leave that house the night of the rape to head home was folly.

My sister was due to come home a day before my prom to help me. My dad was siked to have both of us under the same roof again. My sister had made her life. She was also bringing a guy with her to meet us. She had met somebody that she really liked. When she called home to tell us that she was bringing him, I asked was he really a her. Reminiscing on her prior life before college. My sister was one always going through a fad. Nevertheless, we were happy she was coming and glad to meet her guy. She was staying for two weeks. It was great that my activities were late May and hers was late April early May. My dad and I, along with one of his other daughters, my half-sister and my aunt went up for my sister's graduation. We did not get to meet her guy because he was out of the country on business. My sister met him at her current job. He was one of the promising career figures working for her company. He traveled quite often for the company. He made great money according to my sister and treated her like a queen. Did I fail to say that my sister was a knockout? She just always downplayed herself with dressing tomboyish. I was happy for my sister and hoped that everything would work out for her. She arrived and the party was on.

It was prom day, and the agenda for the day was to turn me into a princess. My hair took the longest. I was the shit. My cousin arrived looking like Denzel, Billy D, Tyrese, Idris, and all the above. Take your pick. We had a lot of people at my send off. The Bentley pulled up and off we went to a night of fun. The last time I attended a school party turned out to scar my life. It was a night of clean fun and laughs. We were amongst the best dressed there. My girl looked good as well. She wore our favorite colour, red. I wanted to stay away from any reminders of that treacherous night. She won prom queen. I was happy for her. She was always exceedingly popular. She was still a cheerleader, fast and smart. She was my girl. Regardless of what had happened. I could not keep faulting her for something she had no control over, knew nothing about and had nothing to do with. On the other hand, her brother was suspect.

Graduation day I woke up incredibly sad. I think throughout the household was a challenge because my mom was not there. My dad, sister and I had a talk at the table while eating before we got dressed to go. I had to be there two hours before doors opened for guest. My dad was going to take me and then come back for my sister, my sisters guy, aunt and half sister. She had been staying with us off and on because she and her mom was not getting along. My sister did not like her. But she was civil to ensure I had a good day. I was part of the honor society. I had worked ridiculously hard the last two years of high school. After the rape, I just studied and watched tv. We went to dinner after the ceremony. I was invited to several parties that I elected not to go. I preferred to hang out with my sister while she was in town. She was heading back in a day or two. The next time I would see her would be in a month when she was coming back to help my dad move me to New York. She was going to miss my trunk party that my aunt was hosting. I was grateful for whatever I got.

The drive to New York was long and tiring. My dad had paid one of his friends with this oversized SUV to drive us there. Boy did that bring back memories. All four of us were drivers. Me the beginner. I had received my license in my senior year. Seeming that I was not hanging out my last two years of high school, my dad had lots of time to teach me. Drivers Education was a cinch. We arrived at my mom's cousins house a day after leaving to get there. We did stop off. I was happy to make it to New York. My dad and those guys stayed the day and over-night. We said our goodbyes and they headed out at about noon the next day. My sister and I cried because we were all going to be sepa-rated. I guess my sister felt like at least when I was at home, dad and I were together. He was now an empty nester for some months. Hmm, I wonder what the walls would have to say when I went home for the holidays. We all knew that my dad would never tell.

"BACKING UP CAN ALSO BE MOVING FORWARD"

CHAPTER 5

A fool for more!

IT WAS A couple of days out before it was time to move into the dorm. My girl was arriving this afternoon. I was so excited. My cousins and I had plan to hang out in Times Square once we got my girl settled. Neither one of us had ever been there. My mom's family was cool for opening their house to me. I was happy because I had also found a job working part time at Top Shop in Times Square. I was excited for the discounts I was entitled to. My girl was going to look for work once she got to town. The evening went cool. We hung out in Times Square. It was a little overwhelming because we were not use to the supersized elements. We did a little shopping for school. My girl grabbed a few applications. One of which appeared promising at this pizza joint. She was ok with it because it was just an outlet for extra cash. She said that she would keep looking until she found something suitable. The weekend passed by fast bringing us to Monday morning the start of my new life.

The class sizes were hugh. We had taken a couple of classes together. General studies to get out of the way. This was a math class with about

200 students. Theatre style classroom. The professor looked younger than what I expected. He was fine. Of course, every female in the class was at him. To my surprise, my girl was not really interested. I think she was still head strong over that looser that had turned her out and mistreated her. I also think that she knew I had a thing for him. One thing for sure, we never had a competition about a guy. Outfits, popularity, and school ranking was more of our struggle. Our professor jumped right in. Where we chose to sit was in eye distance. I do know that he noticed me but did not flinch. He would quite often make eye contact when he was speaking. My girl would nudge me under the table to let me know that she saw the connect. I was looking forward to a student meet and greet session next week after hours. Professors were mandated to be there. Students were encouraged. I knew this would be my only chance to be up close and personal. In my mind I was going to be prepared. Little did I know this was my intro to becoming an opportunist. My girl stopped by my store after she got off work. She had taken that server position at the pizza joint. Her tips were insane. I think men were tipping her on her looks. Whatever worked. She was helping me pick out an outfit for the meet and greet. Top Shop had some cute stuff. I picked out this black dress. Nothing low cut or short, but slightly above the knee, form fitting and classy. I already had red stiletto pumps that would take any outfit to slay. Well, the day came for the meet and greet. I got dressed and looked like a classy sexy professional lawyer. I had my hair pulled back into a ponytail, not over kill, but attractive. The event was held in one of the Student Centers. It had to be over 500 hundred professors and students that attended. They had hor'derves and beverages. When I walked in, I felt the room stopped. I went with two of our guy friends we occasionally hung out

with. Just friends. Nothing physical. They were lots of fun. They fell into the brother category. They too knew that I had a crush on my professor. They also advised against pursuing it. Better yet they did not think anything would become of it anyway. My girl did not attend due to work. She did not want to miss her money. She instructed our friends to snap lots of pics. We wondered around chatting, meeting people, and snacking for about forty minutes before finally laying my eyes on him. He was surrounded by students talking in a circle. This was my opportunity to walk up and join the group. I said to myself, if no sign of interest is made during this time, I would let it be what it was. A mere crush on a teacher. I made my way to the circle and very quietly joined it. Most noticed me. Guys were lusting and girls were rolling their eyes because they were standing there for the same reason. I stood there listening to this boring ass conversation continue for about 20 minutes. With people leaving and new ones joining. Just as I began to think all hope was lost, fate came through. My professor addressed me by name and said, "You look nice tonight MS _____. You have been standing here awhile noticeably quiet. So, what are your thoughts on the matter. Good thing I was paying attention. Here was where I got to show him that not only was I good looking, but I had brains as well. You could tell my answer intrigued him. After speaking I wanted to leave him thinking. I said, thank you professor for allowing me to speak. I then left his circle. I could feel his eyes follow but switched back before it was obvious, he liked what he saw. To my surprise, he knew my name. When I arrived back at the dorm my girl had made it home from work. She wanted to know all the details. We stayed up talking for hours. Keep reading, I will eventually become that woman you met in the first novel, "The Woman Tells."

My groundwork had been laid. After class, the professor asked if he could have a word with me regarding one of my quizzes, I turned in. My girl under her breathes went hmmm. I told her to shut up. I told him, "Sure." But I have a class I must attend right after this one. He asked if I knew where his office was. I said yes. He told me to meet him there at 4 after he was done with teaching his classes. I said OK, it's a date. I caught myself to say I'm sorry sir, it's a session. He chuckled and turned around to the next student waiting to chat. My girl also had the next class with me along with a break after our next class. When we walked out, she said to me. Don't wear any panties y'all may have limited time. You don't want to waste it having to remove too many clothes. I started hitting her. 'Girl you crazy." I failed that quiz and he's going to let me make it up. My girl said. He's going to let you make it up alright. Immediately after my class ended, I headed to his office. There was another student in, so his admin told me to have a seat. Finally, the door to his office opened and I went in. He asked me to have a seat. My heart was pounding. He started to go into my last quiz results. To my surprise, I aced it. So, here is where the shenanigans began. He started to look at me with lustful eyes. I was a little frightened and turn on all at the same time. He started to ask had I ever dated an older guy. One word led to another. Nothing happened, but I was convinced he was mutually attracted to me. During the conversation he did discuss tutoring me. Although I had aced the quiz, my average was not stellar. We agreed that my sessions could be at the library in Times Square not too far from my job. According to him he also lived close and could do it on the way home. Our sessions went on for several weeks. He tutored me in between the flirting. We spent time getting to know each other. And then, it happened. It was one gloomy day, I got called off work. It was slow and he had lots of papers to grade. It worked out perfectly. He offered me a solution to come over to his place. According to him this would save him time. His reasoning was he could do both allowing him to save time. Well, I agreed to come. I arrived too the great smell of some spaghetti and garlic bread. He had papers everywhere. Pots filled the sink from cooking. I asked if he was at school today? He said no. He informed me that some days he did not have to physically be present in a classroom. He was allowed to work from home a few days a quarter if he chose. That explained everything. He had been home all day. So, to get to the point and make a long story short, it finally took place. One thing led to another, and it was on. I was young but I was an enthusiastic person. I was not a virgin so that made it comfortable. He asked was I. He began to rub me and remove my clothes. His hand began to caress my girl and his finger was inside me. Before I knew it, I was on his bed, and he was kissing my girl. We continued to exchange intimacy until finally he was inside me. He was super passionate and gentle. Yet he had a Mandingo movement. This went on for about an hour and a half. We finished, took a shower together and I got dressed. We ended this day eating the spaghetti. He drove me back a couple of blocks from the dorm. I was truly seeing stars. I shared it with my girl when I got back. She was listening carefully and excited. We were laughing, hanging out and drinking. While talking with my girl, he sent me a text to say he was thinking about me. He also had discussed being discrete. He was a professor and was not supposed to be fraternizing with students. He could lose his job. Our little secret romance went on for several months. Each encounter getting increasingly freaky. He started too not be so nice and gentle. He had started to talk about that there were ways he knew that I could make some more money if I were interested. He knew a lot of girls that did it to help with college. He would also always ask how my girl was doing and did she know about us. He even went as far as to say I could bring her with. I felt a bit funny when he said it. I would occasionally catch him watching her in class. We all knew that she was pretty as well.

School had ended for the year, and I had decided to stay over the summer. If you took two classes, you could stay in the student housing. My girl stayed as well. There was nothing really going on at home. I had fallen for my professor, I loved NY and my cousins had invited me to stay with them if I needed to. My dad was ok with it. It didn't matter if he did or not because legally, I was an adult. I can remember the day I was over to the professor's place and was in his bathroom. I saw some female glasses on the counter. I bought it to his attention, and he got an attitude. However, he claimed they were his sisters and that she had stopped by. We never really discussed his family make up. He did say that he had a daughter and that he and the mother was not together. He asked if I was ready to quit that weak ass job and make some real money. Of course, I was curious. He told me that a friend of his had a club and they hired girls to wait tables or if you could dance you could make a lot of money. I asked what kind of club. He said a gentleman's club. He said if your girl was interested, she could possibly work too. I was very apprehensive, but I said we could check it out and I would invite my girl. Well, keep reading because I'm sure you know where this is going. Each chapter I tell something that happened to me during my life. Most things I had no control over, but this one I should have known better. With that said, I will tell.

I had talked to my girl; she was all for it. She had heard about these clubs and how much money the girls were making. She knew more than me. She said you could bartend if you knew how. They made great tips. You could wait tables and they made generous tips. But the real money was the last two. You could dance or become an escort. The latter paying the most. She went on and on that we were young and in a city that no one really knew us except people on campus. She also went on to talk about my boy was just trying to look out for us. He loves me. Bla, Bla, Bla. If your mom or whomever have told you about bad influences, she was one. My older sister never really cared for my girl because she said that she was that influencer and not a good one. I was extremely uncomfortable and doubtful. Here was the kicker, when we met with the professor to discuss it, it seemed like they had already talked about it. He said that he would schedule a time to meet his boy at the club and talk to him. My professor sprang on us that the deal for his boy to take us meant he got 20% of whatever we made. I was really taken back. I began to argue with him. I asked, what are you, our pimp? He started laughing and saying "bae" babe you know that I care about you. He let this slip. All the girls I bring to my boy are good with that. It's a business proposal. My girl was still all for it. I was appalled. She was saying let's just try it and see how it goes. I knew it was too good to be true and that I was not the only student he had been with. Well, we met with his boy. We started out waiting tables. We did that all summer. I had to lie to my dad and mom's cousin about where I worked. It was easy because I was staying on campus. We were paired with this one lady that taught girls to dance. School had started back, and the professor was becoming less and less available. I noticed that my girl had begun to act funny as well. We did not work the same days at the club like we use to. She was getting more hours. We both were dancing now. Classes were hard because I was up all night then trying to make it to class. My off days were spent trying to study. My girl had decided on a single room this year. I still needed to share and have a roommate because I was making more money for sure, but I was getting less days. According to the club owner, I needed to agree to do the escort part to get more days. I asked why my girl was getting more days. To my surprise she was doing the escort part. I just could not bring myself to do that. Talking to the other girls that danced. They said, kid you don't want to do that. It's dangerous and degrading. They also told me that your girl isn't your girl. I never knew why they were saying that until one day I decided to visit the professor without warning during his scheduled office time. His office was in a building that was for professors. Most of the time it was not a lot of professors in their office's certain times of the day. So, I went over to his office to find he was not there. I was really starting to be heartbroken with how he was treating me. I had been living up to the business arrangement. The only benefit was that I did not have to work as many days as when I was working at Top Shop. Not by choice. The extra money balanced out the lack of days. I had seriously thought about quitting and going back to doing something else. I had decided to walk over to my girl's single room to see if she was there. We had not spoken in a couple of days. We did not have any classes together this semester and I needed to talk to her about my relationship with the professor. Well, I had to stop off by my dorm room to grab my girls spare key just in case she was not there. I would stay and chill on some privacy shit. Well today was another life changing event. When I came to the door of her apartment, the music was loud. I asked myself, do I let myself in? No, it's not what you are thinking. To my surprise, it wasn't. I walked in to find my girl fucking her brother and one of the guys that had participated in my rape. Her brother was doing oral on her and one of the guy's that had violated me was having her brother from behind. I thought I was going to be sick and throw up. They did not hear me enter so when I walked up on her. I startled them. All I know is that I turned and ran as fast as I could. I did not stop running until I made it to the student center. My phone began to blow up. It was my girl. I could not bring my-self to answer her. I went to tell student assistance that I thought I was in danger and that I needed to change my dorm room. In the interim. I called my cousins to come get me. I went there. I did have to give an explanation. I told them about what I had walked in on. Everyone seemed to think that my girl was bad news. My mom's cousin, called my dad. He booked a flight to come towards the weekend. I did not want to return to campus. I never shared about my dancing job. My girl continued to blow up my phone. She was texting as well. I missed a few days of classes. I did not want to see her. I kept envisioning what I walked in on. Of course, I did not return to the club, so the professor had been blowing me up as well. I only had a couple of weeks before Christmas break. I did not plan on returning to Columbia after break. I had applied and put in for a transfer to a school in Atlanta. My dad had family in Atlanta. My grades were good, so I got into school easy. To make a long episode short, my girl and I finally ran into each other on campus. We talked in the student center. She told me a lot I never knew. Her brother was adopted, so he really was not blood, not that it made any difference to me. She also told me that he had been bi-sexual for a long time. They had been messing around occasionally for years since she was fourteen. Too my surprise, she was not a virgin when I thought she was, and her virginity was not lost to the guy in LA. What a fucking liar. She also told me that she was seeing the club owner and that she had started escorting. At the end of the day, she had been my friend. I did not want to see her hurt. I still never shared with her about the rape. Learning more of her family dynamics explained more things about what had happened to me. She told me that her brother and his guy flew up to see her for a day and that there was no need to be nervous. They had gone back home. I decided since we were sharing, I did tell her that I was no longer going to work at the club and that I had applied for another school in Atlanta and would be leaving and not returning after break. She was heartbroken, but I knew I needed to change my surroundings. I was still confused and nervous about the professor. I explained that I only came to her apartment to talk about him and that situation. It turns out that my girl knew that he had moved on to another student. She began to make me know who she was. She had learned that this was what he does. He had gotten two other girls' jobs as well. Ones that I was familiar with. Both had dropped out of school. These were the ones that were saying she was not my friend because she knew about the professor. She could only apologize and ask was our friendship damaged beyond repair. I told her I would think about it. But it didn't matter because I was leaving. She also sprung on me that the professor was still married with a daughter that I knew about. The apartment that I would come to was shared by him and the club owner the dude my girl had begun to sleep with. They called it the "Bat Cave." I told my girl not to tell the professor that I was leaving. She vowed that she wouldn't. I asked if she was going to continue at the club and why was she prostituting? She replied because that's all it was. She tried to justify it, but I told her. Please be careful and just know he does not care about you either. It was time for my mom's cousin to pick me up. I was to leave in a week. Little did I know that that would be one of the last times I would talk to my girl. Stay tuned because I will tell.

BEAUTY IS WHEN YOU ARE COZY IN YOUR OWN SKIN

CHAPTER 6

The phone Call

I WAS HAPPY to leave New York after what had transpired in the last week I was there. I was content that I at least learned more things about my girl and her family dynamic. I also got to spend an amazing night partying before I left. We once again dressed up in these tight-fitting red dresses and heels, went to dinner and went to a real young adult club to dance. A few of our college friends went as well. It was about ten of us. My girl had put it together as a going away party. She said that it was not goodbye, she would just have to catch me back home. Two days later after my good-bye dinner, she was shot in the head and left in a hotel room. I was mentally fucked up. Everything happened as you would imagine. Family, school, funeral and on to the next phase of my life. I never started school in January. I took off a whole semester and went to go stay with my sister for a couple of months. It was a breath of fresh air. She was doing quite well. We bonded. My dad came up for a week as well. It was good to be with what family I had. I was leaving for Atlanta after staying with my sister. I felt, to be so young I had bounced around like a ball. Tragedy after tragedy, mishap after mishap. It was time for some positivity and great vibes to come my way. Once again, I was preparing to leave for Atlanta. This time I would not be staying on campus. I was originally supposed to stay with family, but my dad had found another job in Atlanta. He had been dating some lady there for some years and decided to get more serious. Who knew? Also, my half-sister was moving with us too. This would be interesting. We rented a house with the option to buy. It was the nicest place we had had yet. Atlanta houses were cheaper. We all had our own room. The house had four bedrooms. We used the extra room as a office. It was our version of a family. This new school was not as live as NY, but it was fun. I was focused and trying to complete what I had started. I made a few friends. My partying was kept to a minimum. It was one Friday, that my girls brother reached out to me. I was shocked when I heard his voice, but I took the call. I was incredibly nervous because there was a lot of unspoken things that had gone on in our lives that we never spoke about. The first thing that we finally talked about was his friends that assaulted me years ago. He admitted that he knew. He claimed that when it was happening, he was unaware. He said he found out several days after the incident when they were laughing and joking about it like it was a game. I do believe that he was afraid of them because they were the neighborhood thugs. I did ask why he waited so long to talk to me about it. I shared how fucked up I was, pregnant and had a STD behind that. He claimed to be so sorry. He also said that later his boy said that he was wrong to do that. I replied yeah, I thought I was kind of a little sister or something. I did share that I thought he had a thing for me himself and that I did not know he swung both ways. We also spoke about he and his sister's relationship. Adopted really? You never mentioned it. He admitted that he did have something for me, but more for his sister. It was most definitely perverted in my eyes. He said that his life was complicated and that he had to figure it out. Starting with his sexuality and who he really wanted to be. I was happy to put closure to that part of my life regarding the rape and learning that he really did not have a part in it. The next conversation was quite easy to bring up because we were already talking about the act itself. I had to address what I walked in on. The phone got quiet. I think that he was embarrassed. I said to him I guess you were still trying to choose a side, but that was your sister. He immediately spoke up to say, that she was not his biological sister and in the scheme of things you could not call it the "I" word. He explained that it had been going on a while. He expressed that he did care and love his sister. He explained, after the incident happened when I walked in on them, they agreed to stop. Yet, he made the decision to continue to "Boo up" with the criminal that had raped me. He did say that he was just having fun and that one day he did plan to try to have a family, get his shit together and move out of his parents' house. I said I would believe it when I see it. The last part of the conversation was very tough. I asked if they had found out what happened to her. He began to tell me that she had been doing things that was not cool. She had shared with him about the club she and I had worked at. He also knew about the club owner and professor. He said that he too had tried to get her to stop and quit. She had gotten to tied up with these guys and what she was doing was not safe. Mentally or physically. He talked about she had started to neglect school and was not calling home like she should. He did ask me had I gone as far as she did. I told him no. I was just a server there and occasional dancer. He had lots of questions how we even got started.

49

I shared about my relationship with the professor. I admitted that part of me felt guilty about her death. We were introduced to that lifestyle through him. I felt that she would have never met the club owner had I not allowed the professor to manipulate us. Everything had been over the news what happened to her. It was merely a trick gone wrong. As we continued to talk, he expressed that it was not my fault. She made those decisions to chase money thinking that there was an opportunity at play. He said that I was always the levelheaded smart one to go only as far enough to reap some benefits and pull out before it struck dangerous. He said that he wanted to speak to me after the funeral, but everyone was so torn up. It was not the right time. The only thing he regretted was that they never caught who shot her, the professor was still teaching, never hauled in because the club owner and his relationship was kept clean and invisible. The club owner was questioned but it all lead to nothing. It did come out that both the professor and club owner were married men with children. I had been on the phone with my deceased girl's brother way over three hours talking about everything, how much we missed her and just talking about the neighborhood in general. He talked about visiting me in Atlanta. I told him that phone calls every now and then would be ok. I was trying to move on. I also vowed if I visited there again, I would let him know so that we could meet up and have lunch or something. I told him to take care of his parents, tell them that I said hi and to most of all take care of himself because that is what she would have wanted. We hung up and I just laid for a while thinking and reminiscing about everything. In my mind that was closure to a lot of things. RIP is what I said to myself before taking a nap never to talk or tell what happened.

CHAPTER 7

We meet, we merge, we marry, we meet

A FEW YEARS had passed after that long phone call with my girl's brother. It was graduation night. My sister and her family had come. My dad and his new wife were good, and my looser ass stepsister was doing what she does. My cousins from New York were coming in all to celebrate me. I guess my family was trying to rally around me since the incident with my girl. They had a graduation dinner planned and weekend full of activities to bond. I was in good spirits and excited for this accomplishment. I had a job already lined up and I was dating this guy I met at school a year ago. However, he dropped out to work. He did not finish his degree. He found a job working at an auto plant and was making it work. I on the other hand would be working for a company with benefits. I had planned to move out the first opportunity I got. I've always been one that wanted more. The weekend, graduation and family were all great. I had two weeks after graduation before I was to start my new job. I had worked as an intern at this company over last summer and 1 day a week leading up to graduation. They were so impressed that they offered me a position with their company to start full time after graduation. Life was going well.

My relationship with my dude grew to be very serious. Both of us had been working our jobs over six months when I discovered that I was pregnant. It was without question what our next step would be. We shopped for rings and an apartment. We had decided to move in together. We had decided to get married after the baby was born. I wanted a wedding and did not want to be pregnant walking down the aisle. I didn't give a shit that our baby would be present at the wedding. So, we had a lot to do, and a lot was happening over this next year. He was cool with everything. My concern with him was that he was not as aggressive as I would have liked him to be. I was always struggling to be better and make something of myself and he appeared content. We began to plan out the wedding. Of course, my sister was going to be my maid of honor and her kids would be in it as well. He had his best friends and family that were going to participate. Although we were both working. We had to keep it small because we did not have a lot of help. My sister was giving me a wedding shower/baby shower all in one after the baby was born. My dad was helping with the small reception and my cousins from New York who were going to be in the wedding was going to buy the cake. It was coming together. It was something to look forward to. His mom was going to stay at our house so that we could go away for about 3 days for a mini honeymoon. We had vowed when things were better, we would take a full one. Who would think about what's to come and happen after we got married. Like a lot of women sometimes we settle. Ignoring red flags and other warning signs around behaviors and discipline. I guess we get so caught up into the thought of things, getting married, having a baby, and a man, we tend to forget to look at things as they are. My childhood had gone extremely rough; I just wanted the opportunity to have what I called a normal family. He was one that I felt I could do it with. And I was carrying his child. A little about him. He came from a good family background. His parents had been together for years. He had siblings that he was close to. For major holidays they got together and enjoyed each other. He had gone to college and played ball a couple of years but got hurt. He was attractive depending on who described him. He was tall, dark, and handsome. He had a descent build and liked clothes. He had a nice car. I think before me, that's all he spent his money on. I do believe I brought a little discipline to his life. He was like any other single person dating. Keep in mind I said person and not a MAN. I don't think that men have the corner locked on multiple partners. As you know, I was a little wild prior to the rape. However, I did not know that professor's status when I went for him and did not care. I do know that my guy previously did have a girlfriend that he had been with for a while. They were off and on until he met me. I guess I was working with a bit more. Wedding plans were going ok or as well as could be expected working with limited funds and resources. I guess the old saying applied here, "Champagne taste with beer money."

Our wedding day finally came. The ceremony was beautiful. We were young and in love. Family already in full effect with the baby and all. The first couple of years things were ok. Tight but ok. I always lived above my means because I always wanted more. Just when I thought we were getting our heads above water, my husband came home to let me know that the plant downsized, and his job was cut. That was a gut wrench. That meant until he could find more work, everything would be on me. Little did I know is that this pattern would continue. My husband began to take me through a lot of bullshit. Hanging out with his boys so he says. While unemployed, my husband was on child duty. He neglected to fulfill his responsibilities by delegating the babysitting to family, friends and to my amazement, letting her stay at school late. Just all kind of bullshit. He always had an excuse. This went on for a minute. Until I started to become the bitch that you read about in "The Woman Tells." I didn't give a fuck anymore. We were struggling financially. We really were not having sex that often. Originally my husband was all over me with his high sex drive and all. The lack of sudden intimate interest let me know he was fucking around. I said to myself, "Why am I loyal, faithful, paying bills, miserable AND struggling?" I get men coming at me all the time. I am an extremely attractive, married woman. As I quote from "The Woman Tells, I go about my day-to-day business trying to live life to the fullest however it's dealt to me." Not only do men come at me but they also offer me things. Of course, for a little twang, but who gives a fuck. He's enjoying. Let's both have fun. So that's what the fuck I did. I really wish my girl was still living. Man would it be on. I had tried but he started it. The first guy that I messed around with happened to be Italian. He was very well off. I met him when I was working my part-time job trying to help ends meet. Finances were tight due to my husband's sabbatical from work. I'm being sarcastic. Anyway, this guy had come into the restaurant where I was working. I noticed that he kept staring at me. He was with two other gentlemen. I swear that they were extremely well dressed. They looked like something off "Wall Street" or the Mafia. Take your pick. I didn't care because they appeared to have lots of money. My friend, another server noticed how he was starring me down as well. She told me to take their table. Of course, I didn't argue. So, as I walked over to their table their conversation stopped and all eyes were on me. He spoke up to say, hello and that he had never seen me in there before. I told him that I usually work only two days a week. I by chance picked up an extra day this week. He said lucky me. I took their order and immediately ran in the back to tell my girl. Well, the night went well because he left with my number. This motherfucker was fine as hell. He was about 6'1, dark features for an Italian, cold black hair, about 215 lbs., all muscle. I was thinking, I got to get back to the gym. I noticed that he was watching me when I walked away. I think he was watching my wide hips. Man, I was in a great mood the rest of the night.

Eventually he called me a couple of days later and invited me out. Of course, I wore my signature colour. I told my husband that I had a work event. I'm not sure if he cared. So, our night began. He took me to this extremely expensive restaurant and there was where we discussed exactly what our relationship was. He told me that he liked me and was extraordinarily attracted to me. He did express that he was well off and could make things happen for me. The whammy was that he was married, incredibly happy, not looking for a wife. He had kids and would not put them at harm's way for anything or anybody. He said, I see that you are still here so....... He asked me what I wanted. I was honest and shared that I was married, struggling and bored. Before we ended our night and dinner, he pulled a "$1000.00" out of his pocket and said thank you for being beautiful, honest, and nice. There were no strings attached. To me, it was a match made here on earth, not heaven Lol! Did I feel like a "Homewrecker?" NO! "Opportunist Maybe." We went out a few more times before anything happened. The night he rocked my world was something any woman with an imagination would dream up. He liked me in red, so this night I showed back up in a red low cut, side cut out, sheer sleeves bell bottom jumpsuit. He had booked a penthouse on a top floor of this hotel. I could tell when I arrived, he opened the door and he immediately got hard. I know because I could see it through his pants. I could see that he had room service delivered but that came later, because he could not wait. I had never been eaten out so good in my life. He fucked me for about an hour, we enjoyed the room service, he gave me some more money and I left. Each time I was with him was more sensual than the last. I can recall going with him to one of his garages where they housed expensive cars. Yes, he owned a dealership too, where they sold shit like Lamborghini's, Bugatti Veyron's, and Aston Martins. I was floored. This guy was authentic. Well while we were in this hugh garage. He got so freaky. He asked me to undress and to keep on my heels. They were silver. He had to fuck me on top of about four cars. As we finished with one car, he would tell me to walk over to another one. Some he did me from the front, one he gave me pleasure and the other one he was behind me. I would always leave with money. The adventure went on for about 7 months. Did I feel like a whore? NO! I'm just a woman taking advantage of an opportunity to get money. I was having a wonderful time, amazing sex and exposed to things my broke ass husband could not provide. I think I had fallen for him. But the tragedy happened. One day that direct line I had to my knight and shining armor was disconnected. I never saw or heard back from him. I guess my pussy got old. My home life was still crappy. Over the next year or two, I went out with a few others. Nice dinners, conversations, and fun. If they were not putting out or were not able to help me, I didn't fuck with them. I was starting to believe that I was cursed.

Now the story you have been patiently waiting to read about was about to finally unfold. It finally came to flourish ion. The story went something like this. Now let's talk about that no good low-down bastard of a husband from "The Woman Tells." One evening my husband and I had committed to help at this couple's event. We did have friends that we hung with on occasions and had joined this couple's group that we attended when we could. It was a couple's game night. There had never been any interesting people or shall I say, guys there. Keep in mind, my husband and I was going through, not that he would admit to it, but some bitch had begun to call our house and hang up. I was looking particularly good that night. My husband complimented me. That's something that he had not done in a while. At this point we had been together for some years. Shit was stale. Well, it kicked off when this new couple or a couple I had not seen before showed up. I noticed that he was watching me in his own sneaky ass way. His wife appeared to be this bougie bitch in a leather royal blue dress that thought she was the shit. You could tell she noticed the interaction of the eyes between us, but I got to hand it to her, she played it off. She was one of those bitches that spent more time at a mall than fucking her man. I was just the right bitch to help her with that because at this point, I had been through so much until I didn't give a fuck about anybody. I'll water his ass (a quote from The Woman Tells). It was all about me and an opportunity. My chance to really drive the flirting home was when we played this one game. My husband and I happened to be the facilitators for their section. It was a situation that I had to pass out materials. The way the game was set up, the couple had to sit facing each other with a little space in between them. Of course, I jumped at the chance to get close to him. I squeeze through the two of them like I needed to get pass putting as much of my ass in his face as possible. I didn't give a fuck about his girl. Obviously, I acted like it was innocent and played it off. The motherfucker was hard sitting there. You could tell that I had pissed her off. Who cares? Well, the night ended with him getting my number. I slipped it to him when he walked over to get them some drinks. So, I guess I'll wait to see if he's going to call. He took it. Whichever way, I won't tell.

"EVERYONE SAID I COULD BECOME ANYTHING, SO I BECAME ME"

CHAPTER 8

Posh Baby, it's only an opportunity!

WELL, HE CALLED the very next day. Talking about frantic. He was a bit arrogant and old school. He was nice looking. Not as tall as my husband but a descent height. It wasn't like I was looking for the perfect husband because I had one. Our first meet up was at this bar out of the way. We had drinks, sat there, and talked for several hours and flirted. You could tell he came from money the way he carried himself. The talk that occurred throughout the couple's group was the confirmation. He was interesting to talk to. I just had to ask him, "So where is your wife"? He answered, "Probably at the fucking mall." You could tell there was something not gelling between them. However, anything that I asked or any conversations I brought up concerning his wife was either turned off with a short answer or not answered at all. You could tell that information regarding his marriage was off limits.

Our first time sleeping together was ok. He was not that adventurous

guy like the Italian, but solid. He told me how much he was attracted to me and how much he liked my demeanor. He really had
a thing about how I walked and my long hair. Surprisingly, he never
asked about my husband. In a way, it bothered me because he didn't
care, or he really did not care about me. He travelled quite a bit. His
wife never travelled with him. He invited me on several occasions.
Hey of course being married I could not make them all but over the
course of time I made a few. We had an exciting time. I had begun
to really like this guy. He was totally growing on me. And he helped
me out with my bills. I had shared about my husband's lack of work
occasionally. We had been sneaking around for some months. Sex
with him had become very passionate and the thought of messing
around with that bougie' bitches man made me fill like I had paid her
ass back for all the woman she had wronged one way or another. She
was slacking in her responsibilities as a wife because every chance he
got he was inside of me. I can imagine that their sex life had gone
to non-existent. I have to say he and I grew really close over time.
These months had turned into some years of this. I had officially
fallen for the guy. When my husband and I would attend the organi-
zations functions, I would look to see him. My husband was always
somewhere running around trying to be important. Giving me the
opportunity to flirt and tease him. His wife would always give me
dirty looks and my rebuttal was to give her one back that said, yes,
your man is fucking me. I enjoyed making her angry. I was a bold
bitch and didn't care about what she and anyone else in that organization thought. I know several of them were wondering about us
and if we were adulterers. I had begun to tell him that I loved him.
He would always say me too. Never uttering the actual words. We

had been in the same space a lot. I knew that each time I was able
to create chaos in their relationship. An argument on the way home.
I could feel it. However, over time she started to appear as if she
really didn't give a fuck. He had started to become unavailable. I
said to myself, "Is this nigger trying to pull away from me?" I asked
a while ago would he ever consider leaving his wife. His reply was,
"Do you really want to waste time talking about a situation that's
not remotely possible?" He was quick to push it back as if I were the
problem. It bothered me because I had caught feelings. Maybe I
needed to slow my road because what really would become of this.
Who could tell?

It was a great getaway for me and the family to go to Vegas. My sister
had planned this big birthday party for her husband and asked us to
come. We had been planning this for a while. But my mind was not
there. Of course, it was on my extracurricular activity. My husband
was trying to act married this weekend and like a father. We had a
cool room. We stayed at "The Paris." Our kids, my cousins' kids
and my sisters' kids were all in a suite camping out with my stepsister. The couples, my mom's cousin from NY, my dad and now
my stepmom had their room, my sister, and the birthday boy and
of course me and my husband all had our own rooms. Sadly, I had
to sleep with my husband that weekend. He was really appearing
to try to have a suitable time. But I knew in my heart his little side
piece was still somewhere around. We had been through a lot. All I
could think about is what I was going to wear to an event the couples
were having the following week when I got back. I had planned
to find a dress while in Vegas. Something red would be great. The

weekend was going well. We got there on Thursday. The trip was to be from Thursday to Monday. We had something planned every day. Thursday was the travel in day. Although most of us got there early. Friday night was the actual birthday dinner at this restaurant inside the Paris. Saturday night we had tickets to a Vegas show and afterwards the adults were going to party. My stepsister tagged along with the couples dateless. She was harmless. We kept telling her we were going to find her a man in Vegas. My dad and his bride hung back with the kids. They took them for ice cream and to watch the Treasure Island Pirate Show. Nevertheless, it turned out to be a great weekend. That Sunday everyone slept late. My sister and cousin decided to roll with me to find a dress for next weekend. Here is where I missed my girl that passed. No one knew my secret. This is not something I could or would share with anyone else but her about my affair. I did find one at this little funky boutique. It was black. It fit like a glove and was Heller sexy. I could not wait to where it. The entire family had one last dinner in Vegas. Afterwards we headed to Old Vegas to have fun. The next morning we all flew out.

It was the evening of the event. I was getting myself prepared. My husband was getting dressed too. I must admit, he looked handsome. I could not wait to get there to see him and fuck with her. Although lately it didn't appear to have any effect on her at all. We finally arrived late. I could see they were already there. They were preoccupied with this new couple. Jesus! The guy was fine as hell, but he was with someone. The lady he was with appeared to be very attractive as well. I said to myself, maybe I'll talk to him. When I scoped my lover, he appeared to be annoyed and running behind his wife. I instantly got pissed. On top of that, he had the audacity to dance with her. I really felt some kind of a way. I was starting to feel like shit. I really thought he loved and was feeling me. I had been with him several years now, in the cut. But.... I knew in that very instance, there is where he was going to keep me. I didn't give a fuck about my husband. Not after all he had put me through. I'll talk about that in my next chapter. However, I had no right to feel any kind of way or a legitimate cause to be angry. I was married and so was he. He showed me who he really cared about. The way the situation appeared, it looked like it was something with his wife and that nice looking guy. The guy seemed to be into my guy's wife. The guy was ignoring the lady he was with. I started to really tune into what was going on. When dude's wife walked off. I watched the handsome guy zero in on her ass as she sashayed away. This was some "Payton Place" bullshit if I had ever seen it. My lover totally ignored me the entire night. I was highly upset. I had gone to the restroom to try to get it together. On the way out, I saw the handsome guy and his date leaving. One thing about it, I said to myself, if she's fucking with him, she definitely has great taste in men for sure. That motherfucker was even more gorgeous up close. He was about 6'4, about 260 lbs. and muscular not overdone but right and fair skinned. He almost looked Indian, Iranian or something. But back to my situation, I was hurt, pissed, and confused all in one. I was not in a good place. I will continue to tell.

"SOMETIMES PEOPLE ARE PLACED IN YOUR LIFE TO MAKE UP FOR OTHERS"

CHAPTER 9

HOMEWRECKER?
It takes one to handle one!

AFTER THAT TRAGIC night at the event and to add insult to injury the last straw was what happened two days after. One evening while sitting in the kitchen with my husband having another discussion about bills due and me feeling overwhelmed with having to be the bread winner, the doorbell rang. It was his woman that had been calling our house asking if I knew where my man was. Like I said in the novel "The Woman Tells", he and I had been going through. This woman had taken the liberty to send me a pic of my husband asleep in her bed. We went back and forth with him making up ridiculous lies about it was his boys house where they were. And long story short, he said that there was a chic there trying to get with him. He claims she must have gotten mad when I told her that I was married. Total bullshit. It was his bitch at my doorstep. This woman was off the chain. Not only did she send a pic, but she also described my house to me as if she had been inside of it. I can't prove it, but she had too much information. And the ultimate was that she was at my door now. Let me ask, "What does it sound like to you reader?" I opened the door and there she was with a baby. She reminded me of my boo thing's wife. A ghetto version. Well, this hoe pushed past me, sat the baby down and started swinging at me in my house. By the time my husband made his way from the kitchen. We were already fighting. I could not believe what was happening. This was some "Lifetime" shit.

Apparently, she was very upset and like I said in book one, she was yelling take this bastard baby. I was swinging, crying, crushed, and going off too all in one. She was yelling out, "Your son is now going to live here with you playing house with this bitch.' This girl could not have been any more than twenty-five on a good day. This was the chic that sent the pic of my husband in her bed. My husband was trying to break us up. Luckily, my daughter was there and called the police. Another child? He already had one that had moved in with us that he had prior to me. I was bleeding because she had scratched me. We both had ripped clothes. This bitch also smelled like weed. I can imagine what happened. She probably got high. Started thinking about things, took tough pills and made her way to our house. At this point, I didn't know if I was going to be able to bounce back from this. The police arrived and arrested her for trespassing and assault. They could not get her on abandonment because she was still there. They took her to the station. I was definitely pressing charges. My husband spent the rest of the night trying to explain while I was packing. My daughter had the baby. He was an innocent baby boy. Shit just always happened tragic in my life.

Several months had gone by. It was confirmed to be my husband's child. I had to accept the baby to keep my marriage or I could walk away and pursue something else. My affair with old boy was shaky. I had fallen in love with him. He was somewhat ignoring me, and I did not know whether I wanted my husband for all he had put me through. It took me a minute to get it together, but I decided to try again. Bittersweet. He was doing everything he could to make it right. A part of my heart went with the wind. His baby mama got off with community service and a shrink. My husband had expressed that he did not want to abandon his child and if I could not accept him, then he understood and would have to move on. I was crushed at his words, but I refused to let the baby mama win. I had to suck it up and try to move on. In fact, the baby had grown on me. Originally my daughter helped out a lot because I did not want anything to do with him. But God's got a way of softening your heart. Through all of this, my heart had grown colder towards men and woman. Also, I think that my husband had a clue that I had been messing around as well, but rather than bring up the subject of cheating I think he had a lot to forgive himself. From this point on it became even more about me. I was really weighted down with decisions I needed to make in my life. I had several choices. I could stay with my husband and raise his child or leave him and watch him run straight to his baby mama's arms. I could also leave and continue to be ole boy's mistress or try to convince him to leave his wife and live a life of luxury. However, I was very angry because I had not heard from him. He began to disappear. My mind was racing and full of thoughts of how I should handle ole boy. I decided to confront him. I would continue to try to call him until I reached him. Sooner or later, he would have to answer. I told him I was going to confront his wife. The way it appeared; I might have done her a favor. She seemed to really be into that fine as specimen at the event with the bimbo on his arms. Maybe I should try to get up with him. He looked well off, packing and a lot of fun. I'll get back to the story when I confront ole boy, but in the meantime my husband's baby mama relinquished her rights to the baby. She said if she could not have my husband that she did not want his child. I could tell that my husband did have feelings for this girl and that this relationship had gone on for a while. He was probably promising her shit he could not deliver on. I would not be surprised if he was telling her he was going to leave me. How the tables turned. And what a web we weave. Nevertheless, keep reading because there's more to tell.

"NO ONE CAN DO YOU LIKE YOU"

CHAPTER 10

What! Back the Fuck Up? You Got Me Twisted "Boo"

I HAD FALLEN in love with a married man. I thought he loved me. I think he cared about me a great deal. If I did not cross any lines or ask too many questions about his wife. He kicked me down with money, gifts, and dinners. He even brought me a car. I had to tell my husband I borrowed the money from my sister. Of course, I told my sister that I had a private savings to cover me. My sister would not take to kind to an affair. I think she and her husband had an episode through gossiping with my cousin. I had originally gone into this arrangement with getting some revenge on my shitty husband, punishing a bougie bitch and enjoying a little wining and dining for a change. Besides, forget what ole boy did for me, I liked him because he was a challenge. Regardless, I needed to spend some time with him and to get an understanding just where he saw our relationship heading. I think if he told me to leave my husband, I would leave the baby, my husband, and all. I have always wanted more than the struggle. This was an opportunity. I could care-less at this point about wrecking their home. So, I took the liberty to invite him to meet me at our hideout hotel. Of course, he did not answer me. Was he trying to break up with me by not answering? This motherfucker! I liked him because he was charming, dressed nice, very well groomed, intelligent, deliberate, direct but not rude. But don't get this shit twisted, I was not about to have another repeat situation from a nigger just walking away like the Italian. At least not one I could see myself with. I could be very aggressive and demanding. I continued to call him until he finally picked up and it went something like this. He said, "hello" kind of abruptly. I asked. "Why haven't you been returning or taking my calls?" I could not believe what he was saying to me. He was saying that I've gone too far. I'm acting crazy. This was just supposed to be fun. I said to him, "fun my ass." Why don't you just leave her? I thought you said she was cheating on you anyway. He came back to say. I'm not going to leave my wife. This is over. Don't call me anymore. He was trying to brush me off the phone. I could tell that he was probably at home because he was being very dismissive. I was devastated. He was treating me like I was a two-dollar hoe. All I know is that this was not over. Even if I had to go ring his doorbell like my husband's bitch did me. I needed a time out from everything. My world was on fire and NOT in a dope way. I guess the decision to try to work it out with my husband was the best thing rocking. This arrogant bastard was only out to have fun. It was very clear that he loved his wife. I was only a fill in for the things or time she was not fulfilling his ass. I guess I read it wrong. I guess she had been watering her plant after all. The obvious was that I needed to go home and water my own damn plant and stop looking for love and opportunities in the wrong place. I was hurt. But it was a lesson that you can't come up off someone else's demise. Particularly by wrecking another home or relationship. When it's over it's over. Just leave and take your chances that your decision will work out in your favor.

Several months had gone by and things or shall I say my heart had begun to heal. I was finally getting back to not being depressed. My husband and I had an understanding. He was really trying to work at being better. He had even found another good job. He had the opportunity to relocate. Of course, it would be a promotion and more money. We had a lot to think about and decide. The move would not happen until the new year. However, his decision had to be submitted within the next three months. It would be a move across country. Another change of pace might not be bad, considering his baby mama was still here. I often wondered if he was still talking to her. They shared a son. Speaking of the son, I had grown to love him so much. Despite the circumstances of how he came, on the other hand he added substance to our lives. My husband loved his son. The only weird piece was that he looked a lot like his mom. The family had taken him in. She saw him every blue moon. I hated that my husband had to interact with her. We had full custody, but out of kindness he was firm about he didn't want to just cut her out. He consistently said that he had no feelings for her and that he was only looking out for his son. A couple of times I went along for the exchange. You could tell she had put a lot into herself because she knew that she was going to see him. I had to admit that she looked like she had got her body done. She looked good. She had natural long jet-black hair, tall and sassy. I caught him starring at her one time we were interacting. I felt jealous. She seemed to be a different person. She had pulled me aside and apologized for her behavior concerning our altercation. She also apologized for messing around with my husband. This last time she showed up she was with this very well-groomed older guy. He was about my husband's age. I guess she liked older men. However, they were together and appeared happy. Here was the surprising news of the night. She announced to us that she was pregnant, and they were engaged to be married. I was slightly jealous, confused and in awe. I was thinking to myself, "Are you going to give that one away too?" Well, there was one more thing she said that she would like us to consider. It was to give her baby back. She wanted us to consider joint custody. Lord have mercy on this situation, I knew at that moment I was in the twilight zone. My husband and I was so stunned. We had to catch our breath before the rebuttal. He went off. "What the fuck?" She started laughing. She said it was a thought but if we were opposed, she understood. However, she stated that she would like to increase her time with their son. She wanted their child that was on way to be in his or her brother's life. The guy she was with seemed like a cool guy. Apparently, he had money. My husband seemed a bit intimidated. By the time we were parting ways we had agreed to work something out. Later that night after I got in, my phone rang, and it was ole boy. He said that his wife had separated from him. Stick around for chapter eleven and I will tell.

CHAPTER 11

Pleasure in the Sky!

As I MENTIONED, I had just got home, and my phone rang. It was ole boy, the married guy I had been having an affair with. The last time we spoke, he told me we were over. So, you can imagine I was not very welcoming to that bastard. He started off by asking, "How are you doing?" Of course, I said OK. Because I was doing ok. He said that he wanted to start off by apologizing for being so hard on me the last time we spoke. He said he was stressed from work and that he and his wife were at odds. On top of that, she was home that day and overheard him talking to me. He said that he tried to play it off by saying that he was speaking to one of his employees, but she was not having it. He said that she called him all kinds of liars. She said that she wanted to separate until she could figure out what she really wanted to do. I spoke up to say, I guess I should say I'm sorry, but I would be lying. Then I continued talking to ask, why are you calling me? He went into how sorry he was, and that he wanted to see me. I broke down and I told him that I would. We continued to chat for a minute. My husband had gone to pick up my daughter. The baby was sleep so I was free to talk. He was very open on this phone call. He began to talk about his wife. He felt that she may have been having an affair with the guy at the event. Of course, I played stupid because I wanted to hear the juice. I guess in a way I was flattered he was confiding in me about her because the topic was always kept sacred. He went into how she had been acting, how she was always busy and had things to do. I did not want to push, but I had to ask why he suspected that guy? Because from where I sat, it appeared that a lot of guys flirted with her. It could have been anybody. As a matter of fact, 99% of the time it's the least person you would expect. Women are smart. Your partner will flirt with someone in front of you on purpose to throw you off. She struck me as a slick bitch. He kind of talked on to another subject. We small talked a bit longer and got off the phone. I could hear my husband coming in. Perfect timing. It was interesting to hear from him, but I knew I received the call on a rebound. He was feeling bad or lonely about his separation and wanted me to take his mind off it. My situation was not the best currently. So why not. I could use a gift or two to cheer me up.

A couple of weeks went by before we got together. He invited me to join him on one of his trips. He said in between his meetings I could shop. Flattering! He said once the meeting was over, we could stay a few extra days to enjoy the town. I did express that I was not sure how long I could get away, so I suggested that I met him the day it was over. That would probably be better all the way around. It worked out. But the weirdest thing happened to me on my flight down. What a fucking surprise! The Italian guy and his woman happened to be on my flight. I had not seen this ass since he disappeared. It was not a packed flight. As I was walking to find my seat, I noticed him. He looked up to see me. It was strange as hell. He was with some Asian model type chic. She would remind you of that girl who played the rich cousin in that movie, "Crazy Rich Asians." She was pretty. You could tell when I walked past, he felt some kind of way. Might I add, I too was looking fantastic. I was on the way to see my "Boo thing". What would you expect? Well, I'm going to jump right into the wild part. As you may recall, he was the adventurous, total gorgeous romantic playboy I fell for. He disappeared. He was one of the best fucks I had ever in life. That's saying a lot. Long story short. I watched him get up to go to the restroom. He could have gone to the one in the front that was closer, however he elected to come my way. He walked pass and shook his finger motioning me to say, "come here." The stage was perfectly set. The flight attendants were doing their thing up front. The lights were out. Most of the few passengers travelling were sleep or preoccupied. Might I add another point, it was a late evening flight. Well, he summoned me and kept walking towards the restrooms in the back. I waited a minute because I was thinking. What in the hell did he want? To say I'm sorry? Strangle me in the bathroom or something? As I mentioned in the earlier chapter, I always thought he was part of a mob. Nevertheless, I got up to go see. I opened the first side, and it was empty. I knocked on the other side, the one across from it. He opened the door. I squeezed in. He looked at me and said I know you are mad. I'm sorry. It had been a long time. I said I was upset at first, but I moved on. I did ask him had he not seen me on the flight would he have reached out. He was honest, he said probably not. He said that his line of work had gotten hot and he needed to concentrate. I was very distracting. Like now. Wow! Out of know where he asked if he could see me again. I had to remind him that I was a big distraction. He said, it had nothing to do with me. He needed to be disciplined and his wife had begun to question him. BINGO! There it was. Another wife. To answer his question, I said NO that I didn't think so because my life was too complicated, and he too would be a distraction for me. He spoke up to say. Well, can I fuck you now? He went straight in for the kill. I was stunned, turned on and ready to go. He told me to stand on top of the toilet so that he could slide under to sit. He most definitely did the rest to get the party started. A flight attendant knocked to ask if everything was ok. He replied, just a little sick, I'll be out in a minute I'm taking my medicine. I followed all of his instructions. Again, he slid under me and sat. He began to remove my undies. How convenient was I? I had on a skirt. He began to kiss, and lick, my girl. Caressing me and telling me how much I turned him on. It was very passionate. I could feel those tucked away feelings rising inside me. Along with his finger and tongue. Once I reached ecstasy, he pulled me down on him and to my knees and before I knew it, the tables had turned. He began to moan kind of loud. We changed positions and he was inside me. All ____ inches. I'm not sure if his girlfriend was blind, stupid, crazy, or just inconsiderate, but we were gone awhile. She never came back to see if he was sick or anything. We kissed and hugged. He said that he would always think about me. He left me in there cleaning up. When I got back to my seat. He had written his number down and left it there. The message said forever. You are a welcomed distraction. If you need me, call me. I'll work it out. I was in La-La Land. We finally landed. I had a carryon. I did not have to go to baggage claim. Although it took everything in me not to go get a glance at the man that had given me pleasure in the sky. I felt it best just to gather my bag and go. I was sitting towards the back so when we deplaned, he was already gone.

My boo had sent a car for me. The only thing I could think about was the situation that had just taken place on the plane. All I know is that I could not sleep with my boo tonight. I was officially without question a homewrecking opportunist hoe. There was not a fucking maybe to it.

Stay tuned my lover will tell the rest in his spill in Book 4. Yes, I can count. Honor students remember. If you are wondering why not book 3? That's about the handsome guy, the wife's "Boo" or Paramour. I think he has some shit to tell too! He'll explain where the fuck he came from, chapter 6 in "The Woman Tells."

CHAPTER 12

Accountability

THE BIGGEST TAKE away is to remember that just because your circumstances may not be what you feel is the best, does not mean that you can't overcome it or not be held accountable for your actions. Many times we try to blame our surroundings and the hand that we are dealt on other people. Using them as the scapegoat. But in essence, it's nobody's fault but your own if you allow it to be your story. We are responsible for our own destinations and success. Choosing revenge and other get back at you tactics only puts the wear and tear on you. Score keeping and one ups. Are you really winning? When things happen, "Duck & Swing", disappear and set in motion a plan to move on or establish and bring to flourish-ion your dream, idea, or plan. Go for your own. Everyone has a talent; You must discover yours. It may not be the obvious one like singing, accounting, or painting. Maybe it's listening. Psychologists make a lot of money. Just saying. I'd like to leave you with some statistics. On thoughts on the pros and cons of being a mistress. You decide. Don't worry, I'll state the statistics for the paramours or male mistresses in there series.

A Dr. Marni Feuerman a licensed psychologist wrote 10 harsh facts about being in love with a married man; The question has always been since the beginning of time, "Will he ever leave his wife?" Dr. Marni wrote:

- If you are in love with a married man and hope that he will leave his spouse, I have bad news to share. Being in love with an already attached man is difficult. Especially when most people view a woman who they know is having an affair with a married man as a heartless Homewrecker. There is not a lot of scientific data, but the most recent statistics show that only 3%-5% go on to divorce their wife and marry their mistress.

CONS
1. Your relationship is already off to a troubling start
2. Good husbands do not cheat on their wives, meaning that he's probably not a good guy anyway, there are circumstances and exceptions to every rule.
3. You have been living in a fantasy world
4. You don't know what it's like to be involved in his day-to-day life, he could be a straight narcissistic ass hole
5. He may realize that you are not right for him
6. His extended family, children, friends may dislike you etc.... may not ever accept you
7. His former wife will always remain in your life if there are children
8. You may never be able to trust him
9. You will forever be branded as the other woman or mistress
10. You may feel extreme culpability over what happened

She wrote that there are exceptions to every rule, 2 of them. The rest 3-10 were some reasoning, gathered through surveys and research. This information targeted was based on if you even cared about the possibility that the married guy would leave his wife. If your objective was simply for personal gratification and pleasure, the information was not considered.

PRO's

Dr. Feuerman wrote:

1. If he leaves his wife, he left because he was leaving anyway, and you were not the cause
2. You are not putting your life on hold waiting on him

Research & Survey Results

1. There is an understanding on what the situation is, and both agree, neither wants a commitment. You get to keep your independence
2. You give mutual pleasure to each other mentally and physically. You enjoy each other's company
3. He takes care of your needs, wining, and dining
4. You don't have to take care of the domestic things for him if you don't won't to, you don't have to put up with his shit on a full-time basis
5. Friends with benefits
6. It's adventurous and fun
7. Confidante
8. Financially

In conclusion, as written in "The Woman Tells", life is all about what you make it. Goals and dreams can come true. However, you must be willing to see it through. As we continue in "I'm not a Homewrecker, Opportunist Maybe, we see that doors we're opened, some closed, some unlocked waiting to open or close, and some open, still waiting on what's to come. Some relationships are made in heaven. Some generated from nothing and are just meant to be. As such, meant to be does not necessarily mean forever. As I previously quoted, some are merely to teach a lesson. Like the characters in my novels, you have a choice to choose how you will handle the hand dealt you. Be it with grace and patience, revenge, prayer, walking away or staying. The decision on how you move is yours and your reasoning alone.

"SENSE IS NOT COMMON, NOT EVERYONE HAS IT"

Dictionary

This dictionary was included to help all "uncool" people define slang terms!

Bodied up	nice figure
Chuck Em'	fighting violently
Clique	group, team, friends
Fam	family
Fly	cute, dress very fashionable, jazzy, self-confident
Folly	lack of good sense
Get to it	get started
Groove	back to routine
In a bubble	guarded
Kicking it	hanging out
My girl	friends
On lock	taken care of

Play aunt & uncle	not biologically family through blood and genes
Posh	stylish and elegant
Pushing up on	flirting with
Rain	trouble, tragedy
Shig-diggaty	hell
Shut it down	All attention on you, the best
Slay	best dressed, nailed it
Street activity	side relationship other than a public relationship
Twee	cute and silly
Went to blows	started fighting
Whacked	looser, no style
Woof tickets	threat

Acknowledgments & Credits

Anita Luster –   Proofing

Bianca Garrett –   Model

Elite Authors –   Copy Editing & Formatting

Haider Tawakali –   Model

Jasmine Carter –   Model

Lynn Winston –   Diary Design

Tarita Jones –   Model

Yasin Daulet –   (Flowers Productions) – Mini movie

A Special Thank You!

To the three of you. Thank you for the time spent planning, creating, and executing my many initiatives through strategic thinking and much collaboration. You bring to life my brand. You all are valued and greatly appreciated.

Creative Tray   *Book Cover Design, Graphics & Photography*

Erin P.R. Davis   *Social Media, Editing, Proofing, Public Relations Management*

Keiten A. Davis   *The Relationship Colour Palette Design, Programming & Graphics*

THE

RELATIONSHIP
COLOUR
PALETTE
ASSESSMENT
GUIDE

The Relationship Colour Palette
Guide Overview

DISCLAIMER: This guide is based on an opinion. This is not scientifically based. Your results and how you handle them are not the responsibility or liability of the author.

INSTRUCTIONS: The Relationship Colour Palette Compatibility Guide is a simple process designed to create conversation, thought provoking moments, awareness to self-accountability and fun. This is a tool to help while discovering ways to exist in a relationship through generating a plan to communicate effectively. As mentioned, it is not a scientifically based guide. Thus, it was created with much data gathered through research, surveys, human opinions, and questionnaires. For best practices and usage, please follow the suggested steps provided.

STEP 1: SCAN THE QR CODE
STEP 2: COMPLETE THE ENTIRE QUIZ - you and your partner, friend, spouse or whomever should complete the quiz separately.
STEP 3: DETERMINE YOUR COLOUR
STEP 4: USE THE COMPATIBILITY CHART TO DISCOVER YOUR PERCENTAGE RATING DETERMINED FOR YOUR BLENDED COLOURS TOGETHER. FOR EXAMPLE: RED /PURPLE (HIGH)
STEP 5: READ YOUR RESULTS AS PARTNERS TOGETHER
STEP 6: HAVE A DISCUSSION ABOUT THE RESULTS
STEP 7: MAKE AN ACTION PLAN ON THINGS TO HELP THE RELATIONSHIP IMPROVE.

Compatibility Rating Range	Description
HIGH 81%–99%	You can exist together with minimal problems or conflict. You have the natural ability to live and work together in harmony, sexuality, and intellect. You have well matched characteristics that flow. You basically have similar likes, dislikes, and interest. You are both unbothered by your differences and choices. You communicate effectively and whatever problems arise, you are excellent at working out a solution.
HIGH MODERATE 61%–80%	Occasionally you have setbacks with your problems and conflicts. You can exist together regardless. You work at compromising to help the relationship. You do share some interest in the same things. However, you do part ways on some perspectives, but respect the difference of opinion. You have learned the art of give and take. You have figured out how to communicate. Unlike, a high compatibility rating that share a natural blend of many things, you work a little harder to make it work. Not difficult, but it's not a smooth sailing. Over time it can be a wonderful union.

Compatibility Rating Range	Description
MODERATE 41%–60%	You are right at a 50/50 chance at having the same likes and dislikes. Most of the time communication is work. Misunderstandings happen and not all are worked out in a positive manner. You experience tug of wars with various situations that arise within the relationship. Although you do enjoy each other, the day to day can be a struggle. You spend a lot of time just letting things go.
LOW MODERATE 21%–40%	The odds are against the relationship lasting. By being on the other side of a 50% chance at success, according to your results, your relationship needs lots of attention. Communication can be almost non-existent. You appear to be moving separately instead of together as a unit in your connection if any. Things you did in the beginning of your special link may have disappeared. It's not good, but never say never.
LOW 0%–21%	Heartbreak hotel enough said. You might want to ask yourself, is this worth it? This will take serious time and effort on both accounts. Looking at the odds that's not in your favor, if both can't see the prize, then friends is maybe an option.

The Relationship Colour Palette Assessment QR Code

Scan QR code to begin the Assessment.

The Relationship COLOUR Palette Compatibility Guide

COLOUR	RATING
ORANGE / RED	LOW MODERATE
ORANGE / GREEN	HIGH MODERATE
ORANGE / YELLOW	MODERATE
ORANGE / PURPLE	LOW
ORANGE / BLUE	LOW MODERATE
RED / GREEN	MODERATE
RED / YELLOW	HIGH MODERATE
RED / PURPLE	HIGH
RED / BLUE	HIGH MODERATE
GREEN / YELLOW	MODERATE
GREEN / PURPLE	LOW
GREEN / BLUE	MODERATE
YELLOW / BLUE	HIGH
YELLOW / PURPLE	HIGH MODERATE
PURPLE / BLUE	HIGH

The Relationship COLOUR Palette Compatibility Guide CONT.

COLOUR	RATING
PURPLE / PURPLE	MODERATE
ORANGE / ORANGE	LOW
RED / RED	HIGH MODERATE
YELLOW / YELLOW	LOW MODERATE
GREEN / GREEN	HIGH
BLUE / BLUE	HIGH

Author Karla Davis Luster!

FOLLOW ME PLEASE!

Instagram:
@askkarla_
@shopkarlasklozet

Facebook:
*Ask Karla
*Building A Circle of Friends
*Shop Karla's Klozet

Twitter:
@TheWomanTells

TikTok
@askkarladl

Watch for podcast advertisement monthly
IG & Facebook Live!

The Woman Tells

Make believe and Reality are only steps away from being joined. It makes you think about who's the real me!

Don't miss out on the beginning of this Salacious Romance series of novels........

The Woman Tells can be purchased at the following locations:

Amazon

Barnes & Noble Online

900 North Michigan, Bloomingdales Building 5th floor at "Volumes Bookstore"

Ingram Sparks
www.askkarladl.com

I'm Not A

HOME WRECKER

Opportunist Maybe!

The Diary

I'm not a Homewrecker, Opportunist Maybe!

A diary is a instrument that allows an individual to be honest with yourself by creating and writing down archives of inner personal information. It is a spot and tool that permits you to jot down your thoughts and reflections about things that happened around you, record notes about life's events, special moments, positive circumstances and help to identify areas you would like to work on. You can also use it to make monthly action plans to achieve personal goals and establish future bucket list targets. Preparation is always a great way to assist with accomplishing something. As such, gathering your thoughts to be housed in a diary is also a awesome way to memorialize endeavors you might occasionally like to recall. You should always ask this question, "How can I improve as a person?"

With that said, the INAHOM Diary is set up in a twelve month format. It takes away the 1-31 day numbers therefore creating a free fall recording system that alleviates the stress and pressure to record daily. If you write in it once a month, it's still a great heart searching apparatus. Enjoy!

I'm not a Homewrecker, Opportunist Maybe!
The Diary

_____

_____

_____

_____

_____

_____

_____

_____

_____

_____

_____

_____

_____

"Your vibe attracts your tribe"

_____

_____

_____

_____

_____

_____

_____

_____

_____

_____

_____

_____

I'm not a Homewrecker, Opportunist Maybe!

The Diary

_____

_____

_____

_____

_____

_____

_____

_____

_____

_____

_____

_____

_____

"Beauty is when you are cozy in your own skin"

February

_____

_____

_____

_____

_____

_____

_____

_____

_____

_____

_____

_____

_____

I'm not a Homewrecker, Opportunist Maybe!
The Diary

_____

_____

_____

_____

_____

_____

_____

_____

_____

_____

_____

_____

"Me doing Me"

_____

_____

_____

_____

_____

_____

_____

_____

_____

_____

_____

_____

_____

I'm not a Homewrecker, Opportunist Maybe!
The Diary

_____

_____

_____

_____

_____

_____

_____

_____

_____

_____

_____

_____

"Duck & Swing, disappear to set in motion"

_____

_____

_____

_____

_____

_____

_____

_____

_____

_____

_____

_____

I'm not a Homewrecker, Opportunist Maybe!
The Diary

_____

_____

_____

_____

_____

_____

_____

_____

_____

_____

_____

_____

_____

"No one can do you like you"

I'm not a Homewrecker, Opportunist Maybe!
The Diary

_____

_____

_____

_____

_____

_____

_____

_____

_____

_____

_____

_____

"Love you, Trust few"

I'm not a Homewrecker, Opportunist Maybe!
The Diary

_____

_____

_____

_____

_____

_____

_____

_____

_____

_____

_____

_____

_____

"Sense is not common, not everyone has it!"

_____

_____

_____

_____

_____

_____

_____

_____

_____

_____

_____

_____

July

I'm not a Homewrecker, Opportunist Maybe!
The Diary

"Sometimes people are placed in your life
to make up for others"

_____

_____

_____

_____

_____

_____

_____

_____

_____

_____

_____

_____

I'm not a Homewrecker, Opportunist Maybe!
The Diary

_____

_____

_____

_____

_____

_____

_____

_____

_____

_____

_____

_____

"Sometimes a loss is actually a gain"

_____

_____

_____

_____

_____

_____

_____

_____

_____

_____

_____

_____

_____

September

I'm not a Homewrecker, Opportunist Maybe!
The Diary

_____

_____

_____

_____

_____

_____

_____

_____

_____

_____

_____

_____

_____

"Backing up can also be moving forward"

_____

_____

_____

_____

_____

_____

_____

_____

_____

_____

_____

_____

_____

October

I'm not a Homewrecker, Opportunist Maybe!
The Diary

"Everyone said I could become anything,
so I became me"

November

I'm not a Homewrecker, Opportunist Maybe!
The Diary

December

"Moving in silence doesn't mean you're quiet"

December

Printed in April 2023
by Rotomail Italia S.p.A., Vignate (MI) - Italy